TIGERL

NATALIE MERCHANT

Amsco Publications
New York London Sydney

Package Design: MISS MERCHANT & FRANK OLINSKY
Portraits of Natalie: DAN BORRIS

This book © 1995 indian love bride
Published 1995 by AMSCO PUBLICATIONS,
A Division of MUSIC SALES CORPORATION, New York

Order No. AM 934439
US International Standard Book Number: 0.8256.1533.X
UK International Standard Book Number: 0.7119.5415.1

Exclusive Distributors:
MUSIC SALES CORPORATION
257 Park Avenue South, New York, NY 10010 USA

MUSIC SALES LIMITED
8/9 Frith Street, London W1V 5TZ England

MUSIC SALES PTY. LIMITED
120 Rothschild Avenue, Rosebery, Sydney NSW 2018 Australia

Printed and bound in the United States of America by
Vicks Lithograph and Printing Corporation

SAN ANDREAS FAULT

Words and Music by NATALIE MERCHANT

CARNIVAL
Words and Music by NATALIE MERCHANT

Additional lyrics

2. I've walked these streets
   in a spectacle of wealth and poverty,
   in the diamond markets
   the scarlet welcome carpet
   that they just rolled out for me.

   I've walked these streets
   in the mad house asylum,
   they can be
   where a wild eyed misfit prophet
   on a traffic island stopped
   and he raved of saving me.

WONDER
Words and Music by NATALIE MERCHANT

1. Doc-tors have come ___ from dis-tant cit ___ ies, just to see ___
2. News-pap ___ ers ___ ask ___ in-tim-ate ques-tion, want con-fes-

23

24

BELOVED WIFE
Words and Music by NATALIE MERCHANT

Slowly

You

were the love for cer - tain of my life,

you were sim-ply my be-lov - ed

wife.

I don't know for cer - tain how _ I'll live my life

gone she suf-fered long in hours of pain. ___ My love is

gone would it be wrong if I should just turn my face a - way ___ from the

light, _ go with her to - night?

poco rit.

RIVER
Words and Music by NATALIE MERCHANT

Moderately fast

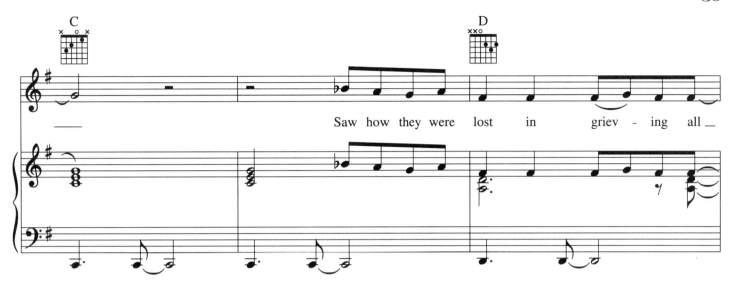

Saw how they were lost in griev - ing all _

_ half be - liev - ing you were gone. Oh the

repeat and fade

loss and pain of it, crime_ and the shame of it, you were gone. _ It was such a
night-mare rav - ing, "how_ could we save __ him from him - self?" _

THE LETTER
Words and Music by NATALIE MERCHANT

Moderately slow, in 2

1. If I ev - er write this let - ter,
2. If I ev - er write this let - ter

oh, the pag - es I ___ could write.
bit - ter words it would con - tain.

42

I MAY KNOW THE WORD

Words and Music by NATALIE MERCHANT

Slowly, with a steady beat

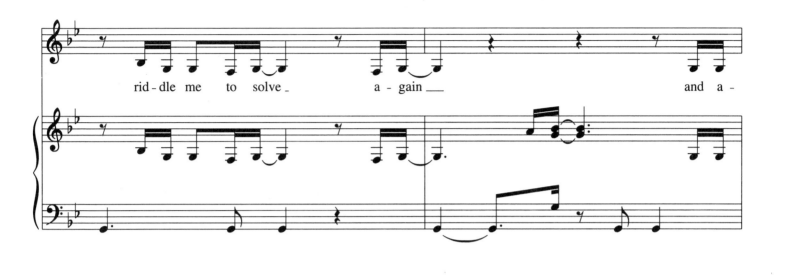

rid-dle me to solve _ a - gain ___ and a -

gain and a - gain

repeat and fade

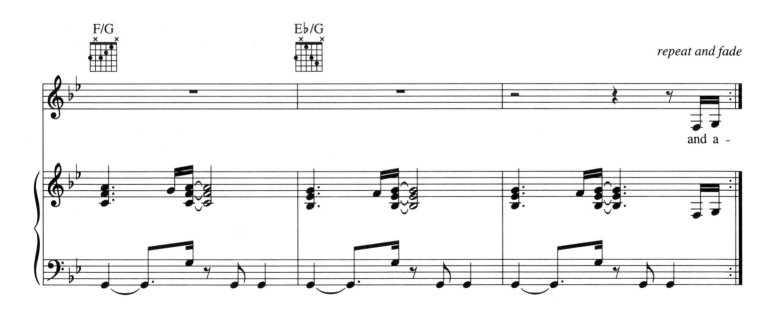

and a -

COWBOY ROMANCE
Words and Music by NATALIE MERCHANT

JEALOUSY
Words and Music by NATALIE MERCHANT

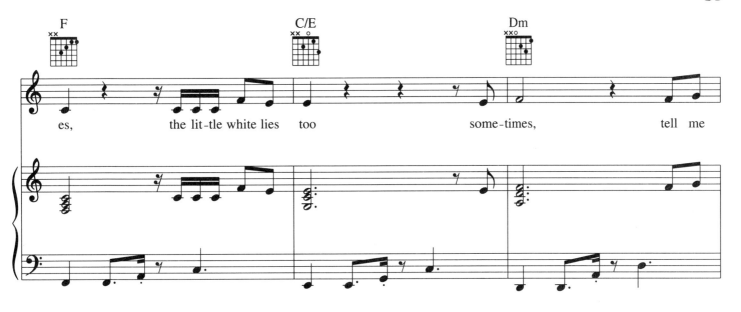

es, the lit-tle white lies too some-times, tell me

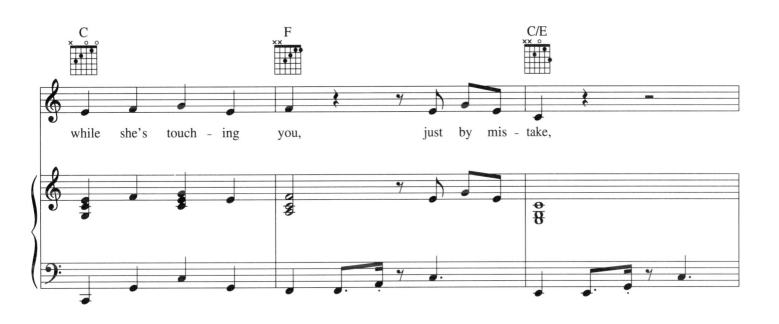

while she's touch - ing you, just by mis - take,

ac - cid - ent - 'lly do you say my name?

poco rit.

p

WHERE I GO
Words and Music by NATALIE MERCHANT

Moderately fast

1. Climb-ing un-der a barbed _ wire fence _ by the
2. Find a place on the riv - er bank _____

rail - road ties, _____
where the green rush - es grow _____

SEVEN YEARS
Words and Music by NATALIE MERCHANT